MANCHESTER CITY SONGBOOK

FROM BLUE MOON TO NIALL QUINN'S DISCO PANTS

MANCHESTER
CITY
SONGBOOK

FROM BLUE MOON TO NIALL QUINN'S DISCO PANTS

Sport Media

A Trinity Mirror Business

MANCHESTER CITY
SONGBOOK

Produced by Sport Media, Trinity Mirror North West.

Executive Editor: Ken Rogers
Senior Editor: Steve Hanrahan
Senior Production Editor: Paul Dove
Senior Art Editor: Rick Cooke

Design & Production: Adam Oldfield
Cover Design: Rick Cooke

First Edition
Published in Great Britain in hardback form in 2012.
Published and produced by Trinity Mirror Sport Media.
PO Box 48, L69 3EB.

ISBN: 9781908695314

Printed and bound by CPI Group (UK) Ltd, Croydon, CR0 4YY

Acknowledgements

Thanks to Will Beedles, Paul Dove, Adam Oldfield and Steve Hanrahan from Sport Media for their encouragement, enthusiasm and belief; to all the City fans who helped along the way, in particular John Barlow, The Blue Alliance, Alan Richards, Andy Burgess, Kevin Mulvaney, Tony Kane, Chris Colesell, Gavin Iredale, Chris Nield, Jack Millington, Dave Sigsworth, Dante Friend, bluemoon.co.uk, mcivta.com, fanchants.co.uk and all the countless City fans who have invented the songs in this book but cannot be thanked personally. There will inevitably be some songs missing – please let us know if you see any glaring omissions – but we think all the major players are in here.

Foreword by Shaun Goater

hen you hear the City fans sing your name, you know you are doing something right. This is a set of supporters who will stick by you through thick and thin – or as one guy said to me once – thin and thinner! Days like that, hopefully, are now gone forever.

I can't remember the first time I heard 'Feed The Goat', but I do remember the lads coming in and telling me how much they liked it. Whenever I heard it after that moment, it always gave me confidence to play my natural game because I knew the fans were with me all the way.

Maybe I wouldn't have scored as many goals I did without that backing – who am I kidding? I know I wouldn't! When I first arrived, I don't think either the fans or myself could ever have guessed what lay ahead and the four years I spent at Maine Road were the best days of my life.

My song took on a life of its own and became famous in its own right but there were three or four others I loved, too. I'll never forget walking off the pitch after we'd beaten United 3-1 in the last Maine Road derby and hearing the whole ground singing 'Who Let The Goat Out?' – a great memory.

Songs and chants are fun but they can also lift you higher and make you believe anything is possible. I think the City fans have come up with some of the best over the years and this collection proves that theory to be correct. I hope you enjoy them as much as I have and remember – feed me and I will score!

Shaun Goater

Introduction

all it gallows humour, self-depreciation or just an ability to take knocks squarely on the chin, but one thing is for sure, you can't keep Manchester City fans down for long.

In fact, for a club that has bounced between the leagues and even slipped down among the dead men into the third tier of English football, Blues' followers have always made the best of things, stayed loyal and backed their team come what may.

And the humour has never been far away...

When City's relegation to Division Two became inevitable during the final game of the 1997/98 season, 6,000 travelling fans at Stoke began to sing "Are you watching Macclesfield?" as thoughts turned to some of English football's least hospitable outposts. It was funny, off the cuff and spoke volumes of the supporters who have become synonymous with seeing the lighter side of life.

No matter what, they were sticking with their team and when others would have deserted in droves, City's crowds actually increased!

The songs remained tinged with irony and opposition taunts of 'You're not famous anymore' would invariably draw some witty response such as the chant at Grimsby that suggested they only sang when they were fishing.

Introduction

Whether it was 25,000 voices in unison singing on a packed Kippax terrace at Maine Road or a rousing chorus of Blue Moon at the Etihad Stadium, the City fans revelled in their role as the twelfth man and that's why the chant from opposing supporters of 'Where were you when you were (erm, not so good!)' – or words to that effect – hold little weight in football. Everyone knows City fans have stuck by their team through thin and thin, shaping a collective body into perhaps one of the most inventive following in the country.

From unforgettable chants like 'Feed the Goat and he will score', to 'Niall Quinn's disco pants', the Manchester City Songbook is the first complete collection of the chants and songs that have lifted the players or brought a smile to the faces of thousands at times when it was needed the most.

When the City fans claim 'We're the pride of Manchester', they do it with just cause.

I've starred out some of the expletives from some of the songs and left distasteful ones out altogether. These are reproductions of songs the City fans sing and in no way are they condoned or encouraged by Manchester City Football Club – they are merely a collection of popular songs and chants from the past and present.

Now sit back and enjoy the songs that have shaped a club and set City fans apart.

Although these are the songs of Manchester City supporters, they are not endorsed the club. This is an unofficial book and the songs within are not meant to cause offence in any way.

Abu Dhabi
(To the tune of 'God Save Ireland')

We're on the march with Abu Dhabi,
We're buying everyone we see,
And we really shake them up,
When we're winning all the cups,
'Cos City are the greatest football team!

*(Tribute to the wealth and homeland of
City owner Sheikh Mansour)*

Adebayor, Emmanuel
(To the tune of 'Sloop John B')

Adebayor, Adebayor,
He cost less than Berbatov,
He scores a lot more.

Adebayor, Adebayor,
He kicked Van Persie,
His face is a bit sore.

*(With Emmanuel Adebayor insulted by almost every visiting
team with varying versions of the same song – City fans
invented their own, more Ade-friendly version)*

Aguero, Sergio

Sergio, Sergio,
Sergio, Sergio.
Sergio, Sergio,
Sergio, Sergio!

Aguero, Sergio II
(To the tune of 'La Bamba')

Kun Aguero, Aguero,
Kun Aguero, Aguero,
He scores for fun, his name is Kun, he scores for fun,
Kun, Kun Aguero,
Kun, Kun Aguero!

*(New City song likely to be heard more at the
Etihad Stadium in the coming seasons)*

Aguero, Sergio III

The hand of God wanted him to join,
Aguero! Aguero!
He didn't just join us for some coin,
Aguero! Aguero!
We bought the lad from sunny Spain,
He gets the ball we score again,
Sergio Aguero rising us to fame!

Aguero, Sergio IV
(To the tune of 'This is How it Feels')

This is how it feels to be City,
This is how it feels to be small.
You sign Phil Jones,
We sign Kun Aguero, Kun Aguero, Kun Aguero.

*(In response to United's belittling song about City, also to the tune of
Inspiral Carpets' 'This is How it Feels', Blues fans suggest
the Reds' transfer targets are somewhat less ambitious)*

Aguero, Sergio V
(To the tune of 'That's Amore')

When the ball hits the net and it's not Torres or Shrek,
It's Aguero.
When your full-back's confused and defence over-used,
That's Aguero.
With the ball at his feet and the movement so sweet,
That's Aguero!

Alan
(To the tune of 'Go West')

Stand up, if you love Alan,
Stand up, if you love Alan,
Stand up, if you love Alan,
Stand up, if you love Alan!

(City fans reacted quickly when Salzburg brought on a sub simply named 'Alan' during a Europa League group stage match at the Etihad Stadium. It led to a raft of songs aimed at the bemused Brazilian – all affectionate – as the Blues coasted to victory in the snow)

Alan II

We love you Alan, we do!
We love you Alan, we do!
We love you Alan, we do!
Oh Alan we love you!

Allen, Clive

One Clive Allen,
There's only one Clive Allen,
One Clive Allen, there's only one Clive Allen!

*(Clive Allen became a cult figure among the City fans during
his time with the club. A natural goalscorer, he fell out with
manager Peter Reid but still had the backing of the fans
– until he was eventually moved on)*

Anelka, Nicolas

Super, super Nic,
Super, super Nic,
Super, super Nic,
Super Nic Anelka.

Anelka, Nicolas II
(To the tune of 'Give The Dog A Bone')

A-N-E,

L-K-A,

Anelka is the player for me,

With a nick nack paddy wack give a dog a bone,

Why don't United sod off home?

Anelka, Nicolas III
(To the tune of 'Bread Of Heaven')

Feed the Elk,

Feed the Elk,

Feed the Elk and he will score,

Feed the Elk and he will score!

(A play on the 'Feed The Goat' chant, Anelka remained at City after strike partner Shaun Goater and inherited the song for a short time)

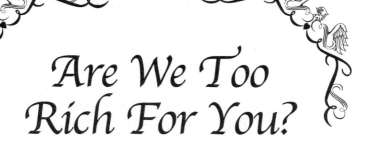

Are We Too Rich For You?

Are we too rich for you,
Are we too rich for you,
Are we too rich for you,
Are we too rich for you...?

(Often criticised for being under the ownership of Abu Dhabi billionaire Sheikh Mansour, the City fans were quick to respond to any chants regarding wealth)

66 When we play away from home, our fans are very loud and never stop singing but we need that at home, too, because that's what the players like. I like Blue Moon but we like it noisy in our stadium so that's my advice to them – more noise please! 99

– Mario Balotelli

Balotelli, Mario

Oh Balotelli he's a striker...
He's good at darts,
He's allergic to the grass,
But when he plays he's ******* class.
Drives around Moss Side with a wallet full of cash,
Can't put on his vest, but when he does he is the best,
Goes into schools and tells teachers all the rules.
Oh Balotelli he's a striker,
He's good at darts,
Sets fire to his gaff,
Shooting rockets from his bath,
He doesn't give a ****,
'Cause he does it for a laugh.
Oh, Balotelli, he's a striker...

*(Cult Italian striker Mario Balotelli has attracted more headlines
than any other during his relatively short time with City. The
stories continued unabated until there was enough material to
come up with one of the most popular City songs since 'Feed
The Goat', encapsulating all his alleged escapades into one,
clever, affectionate tribute)*

Balotelli, Mario II

(To the tune of the White Stripes' 'Seven Nations Army')

Mario Bal-o-telli,
Mario Bal-o-telli!

Bananas!

Bananas, bananas, bananas!

*(Sung during City's inflatable craze in the late 1980s
– simple and straight to the point)*

Barry, Gareth

(To the tune of 'My Old Man's A Dustman)

Gareth Barry is magic,
He wears a magic hat,
And when he saw the blue camp,
He said "I'm havin' that."

He didn't join the Scousers,
Or sign for Arsenal,
He joined the super City,
Because we are wonderful...

*(Having turned down Liverpool and Arsenal, Gareth Barry
was subjected to heckling whenever he played any of the clubs
mentioned – the City fans respond with the above song)*

Barton, Joey
(To the tune of 'Bread Of Heaven')

Can you hear us?
Can you hear us?
Can you hear us in your cell?
Can you hear us in your cell?

(Joey Barton left City under a dark cloud and the former crowd favourite, incarcerated for assault while a Newcastle player, was serenaded from afar as the Blues took on the Magpies at the Etihad Stadium)

Barton, Joey II
(To the tune of 'Doo Wah Diddy')

Who's a blue boy bossin' the midfield,
Joey Barton and he'll put you on your a*se,
Snapping at ankles and tackling everywhere,
Joey Barton and he'll put you on your a*se.
He looks good (he looks good),
He looks fine (he looks fine),
Should be playing all the time...

(On the flip side, Barton also had a decent song to call his own at the peak of his powers with City)

Bell, Colin – Colin The King
(To the tune of 'Lily The Pink')

We'll drink a drink, a drink,

To Colin the king, the king, the king,

'Cos he's the saviour of Man City,

He's the greatest inside forward that the world has ever seen!

(One of the oldest songs City fans still sing,
'Colin The King' is now only aired on special occasions
and always started with an elongated 'Weeeeeee'lllll'
when the chorus is repeated)

Bell, Colin II

(To the tune of 'Yellow Submarine')

Number one, is Colin Bell,
Number two, is Colin Bell,
Number three, is Colin Bell,
Number four, is Colin Bell,
Number five, is Colin Bell,
Number six, is Colin Bell,
Number seven, is Colin Bell,
Number eight, is Colin Bell,
Number nine, is Colin Bell,
Number ten, is Colin Bell,
Number eleven, is Colin Bell,
The substitute is Colin Bell,
The referee is Colin Bell,
The man who sells the pies is Colin Bell.

We all live in a Colin Bell world,
A Colin Bell world,
A Colin Bell world.
We all live in a Colin Bell world,
A Colin Bell world,
A Colin Bell world!

*(The message that Colin Bell WAS the City team for the
best part of a decade is rarely heard these days)*

Bell, Colin III
(To the tune of 'My Old Man's A Dustman)

His name is Colin Bell,
From Bury he did come,
He plays for old Joe Mercer's team,
That's in Division One.

And when you walk down Maine Road,
You'll always hear the cry,
We are the best team in the land,
That no-one can deny.

Bell, Colin IV
(To the tune of 'Jesus Christ – Superstar')

Colin Bell, Franny Lee, Rodney Marsh,
Mike Summerbee,
Score a goal, win the cup,
When you're the best, you don't give a ****!

Bell, Lee And Summerbee

Heigh-ho, heigh-ho, we're off to Mexico,
With Bell and Lee and Summerbee,
Heigh-ho, heigh-ho…

Bellamy, Craig

He's Welsh,
He's ace,
He'll tw*t you in the face,
Bellamy! Bellamy!

Bellamy, Craig II

Bellamy, Bellamy!
Bellamy, Bellamy!

Benarbia, Ali

(To the tune of 'Hey, Baby!')

Hey, Ali Ben-arbia,
Ooh-ah!
I wanna kno-o-o-ow,
Will you feed the Goat?

(Sung to the Algerian genius who had more assists in one season than any other City player in living memory during the 2001/02 campaign – as the song suggests, Shaun Goater fed often with Ali B behind him!)

Benitez, Rafa

Fat Spanish waiter,
You're just a fat Spanish waiter,
Fat Spanish waiter,
You're just a fat Spanish waiter!

(City fans lay claim to this chant – and with good reason – the ultimate managerial put-down for Rafa who, it has to be said, did resemble the character in the song at the time...)

Benjani
(To the tune of 'Volare')

Benjani woah-oh, Benjani woah-oh,
He comes from Zimbabwe,
He scored on derby day...

*(Benjani became an instant crowd favourite by scoring on his
debut for City away to United and helping the Blues
record a first Old Trafford win for 34 years)*

Best Team In The World...

City, City,
The best team in the land,
In all the world (in all the world).

*(An old favourite that has stood the test of time and is
still heard at the Etihad Stadium even today)*

Billion In The Bank
(To the tune of 'Yellow Submarine')

We're going up, we're going down,
We're going up, we're going down,
We're going up, we're going down,
We're going up, we're going down,
City's going down with a billion in the bank,
Billion in the bank, billion in the bank,
City's going down with a billion in the bank,
Billion in the bank, billion in the bank!

*(Blues fans adopt United's chant and rendered it
powerless by singing the same words, bragging
about the wealth of the club)*

Blame It On The Nevilles
(To the tune of 'Blame it On The Boogie')

Don't blame it on Mettomo,
Don't blame it on Wiekens,
Don't blame it on Distin,
Blame it on the Nevilles.

Don't blame it on Fowler,
Don't blame it on Howey,
Don't blame it on Jensen,
Blame it on the Nevilles.

They just can't, they just can't,
They just can't control their feet!

(Not sang that often – this 'tribute' to Gary and Phil Neville has been heard in different guises at various clubs over the years)

Bless Them All

Bless 'em all, bless 'em all,
Bert Trautmann, Dave Ewing and Paul.
Bless Roy Little who blocks out the wing,
Bless Jack Dyson the penalty king.
And with Leivers and Spurdle so tall,
And Johnstone, the Prince of them all.
Come on the light Blues,
It's always the right blue,
So cheer up me lads,
Bless 'em all.

*(And old song sang back in the 1960s when the wit and
wisdom of the terraces isn't quite what it is today)*

Blue Moon

Blue Moon,
You saw me standing alone,
Without a dream in my heart,
Without a love of my own.

Blue Moon,
You saw me standing alone,
Without a dream in my heart,
Without a love of my own.

(Blue Moon is rumoured to have started during an away game at Anfield in 1989, but as with anything as ambiguous as when a song actually began to be sung by the masses, it's no more than an educated guess. Though Blue Moon has also been sung by fans of Peterborough United and Crewe, it became associated with City as it began to be heard at every home game throughout the 1990s until the present day when the song cannot be played or sung by anyone else without the association to Manchester City FC)

Blue Moon – United

Blue Moon,
You started singing our tune,
You won't be singing for long,
'Cause we still beat you 5-1.

(When United fans sang that City fans had celebrated too soon having led 2-0 at half-time in a Maine Road derby, only to lose 3-2, the response was to remind Reds' fans that they'd still taken a beating not that long ago)

Blue Wembley
(To tune of 'White Christmas')

I'm dreaming of a Blue Wembley,
Just like the ones I used to know,
There'll be blue flags flying,
And Scousers crying,
To see, City win the Cup (win the Cup!).

(Sung on the run to the 1981 FA Cup Final and for several years after, the City fans' version of Irving Berlin's 'White Christmas' serenaded the Blues during the FA Cup runs for around a decade. Always nice to hear when there's snow in the air and enjoyed something of a revival during City's 2011 FA Cup run which ended in a 1-0 final win over Stoke)

Blues Are Here...

Blues are here,
Blues are there,
Blues are every ******* where,
Na, na, na, na, na, na, na, na, hey!

*(Sung at grounds where City's sizeable following was forced
to integrate with the home fans in order to satisfy demand)*

Bond, John

We're on the march, we're John Bond's army,
We're all going to Wembley,
And we'll really shake 'em up,
When we win the FA Cup,
'Cos City are the greatest football team.

*(John Bond arrived in 1980 and transformed a team
threatened with relegation into the 1981 FA Cup finalists)*

Born In Gorton
(To the tune of 'Matchstick Men')

We were born in Gorton,
Then we moved to Moss Side,
From there our name spread far and wide.
Everybody's seen the Sky Blue shirt.

From old aged men with hair like snow,
To five-year-olds, with beds to go,
Standing side by side as they watch their team with pride.

And people ask you who you support,
And you tell 'em, but you don't know why,
It doesn't matter if they win or lose,
Just as long as they try.

No Man U or Arsenal for me,
It's Bell, Lee, Summerbee,
I'll be a Kippax Kid, until the day I die.

Boyata, Dedryck

Dedryckkkkkkkkkk!
Boyata, Boyata!
Boyata, Boyata!
Boyata, Boyata!

The Boys In Blue

City! Manchester City!
We are the lads who are playing to win,
City – the boys in Blue will never give in!
Football is the game that we all live for,
Saturday is the day we play the game,
Everybody has to pull together,
And together we will stand.
Even if we're playing down at Maine Road,
Or if we play a million miles away,
There will always be our loyal fans behind us,
To cheer us on our way!

[continued...]

[continued...]

City! Manchester City!
We are the lads who are playing to win,
City – the boys in Blue will never give in.
Blue and white we play together,
We will carry on forever more!
Maybe in another generation,
When other lads have come to take our place,
They'll carry on the glory of the City,
Keeping City in the place..
City! Manchester City!
We are the lads who are playing to win,
City – the boys in Blue will never give in,
The boys in Blue will never give in,
The Boys in Blue will never give in!

*(An original song written by half of the 1970s band 10cc
and sang by the City squad of the day, 'The Boys In Blue'
was recorded in the early 1970s and became the song the
team ran out to for more than 20 years at Maine Road.
Occasionally sung by the supporters and occasionally played
at the City of Manchester Stadium, the song has its place in
the club's history and hearts)*

Brown, Michael

(To the tune of 'Knees Up Mother Brown')

Knees up Michael Brown,

Knees up Michael Brown,

Get those knees up, knees up, knees up,

Knee's up Michael Brown!

*(Sang in honour of City's tough-tackling Academy graduate
Michael Brown who, shall we say, tackled
enthusiastically on occasion)*

66 I'm really happy to be a City player and this club has amazing support. The problem City has had in the recent past has been stability – they'd come up, go back down again and so on – and the fans have suffered a lot of heartache along the way. For them to come out in the numbers they did in Division Two and Division One takes some doing. They've shown amazing loyalty and I look forward to playing in front of them. 99

– Andy Cole

Castillo, Nery
(To the tune of 'Volare')

Castillo...whoah oh-oh!
Castillo ...whoah oh-oh!
He paid his transfer fee,
To sign for Man City!

(Cash-strapped City signed a collection of journeymen strikers, free agents and loan players during the leaner pre-Abu Dhabi days and rumours that Nery Castillo had actually paid part of the fee that allowed him to move to the Blues resulted in the above song)

Chelsea
(To the tune of 'Guantanamera')

Small town in Moscow,
You're just a small town in Moscow,
Small town in Moscow,
You're just a small town in Moscow!

Christmas Shopping
(To the tune of 'Guantanamera')

Gone Christmas shopping,
You should have gone Christmas shopping,
Gone Christmas shopping,
You should have gone Christmas shopping...

*(Sung to Barnsley fans who were watching their team
go in 5-0 down at half-time during a Carling
Cup tie not that far off Christmas)*

City Is Our Name
(To the tune of 'Hokey-Kokey')

We've got an M an A an N,
a C an I T Y,
We've got the greatest football team,
That money couldn't buy.
We come from Maine Road, Manchester,
And City is our name,
City is our name.

City Is The Team

City's the team,
They're the best team in the land,
Playing the game,
Always in command.
We may lose a point or two,
But never do despair,
'Cos you can't beat the boys in the old light blue,
When they come from Manchester.

City Will Win The League (1968)
(To the tune of 'Halls Of Montezuma To The Shores Of Tripoli')

From the banks of the River Ir-Wy-Ell to the shores of Sicily,
We'll fight, fight, fight for City to win the Football League.
To Hell With Man United, to Hell With Liverpool,
We'll fight, fight, fight for City to win the Football League.
We will stop on the banks of the Mersey on our way up to the top,
The right will take the Stretford End and the left will take the Kop.
We will string Fitzpatrick by his balls and we'll paint Old Trafford blue,
Then as we march down Wembley Way we will sing this song to you....
From the banks...

*(A chant borne out of the 1968 title triumph that
was heard for several years after)*

Clichy, Gael
(To the tune of 'Pass The Dutchie')

Pass to Clichy on the left-hand side,
Pass to Clichy on the left-hand side,
Give him the ball and he will run, run, run (he is a Blue),
Give him the ball and he will run, run, run (he is a Blue).

*(One of two classic chants based on old songs
for the popular former Arsenal full-back)*

Clichy, Gael II
(To the tune of 'Dreadlock Holiday')

I don't like Clichy, oh no,
I love him, oh yeah,
I don't like Clichy, oh no,
I love him!

Cole, Andy

(To the tune of 'Camptown Races')

Andy Cole, Andy Cole,
Andy, Andy Cole,
When he gets the ball he scores a goal,
Andy, Andy Cole.

Cole, Andy II

Oh Andy Cole, he's not Man U anymore,
He's not Man U anymore,
Oh Andy Cole,
Oh Andy Cole, he's not Man U anymore.

*(Much-travelled former United striker enjoyed one good
season with City before moving on, but he proved to be more
popular than many people believed he would be
thanks largely to a decent scoring ratio)*

Cole, Andy III

(To the tune of 'Let It Snow')

Oh the team we're playing is frightful,
But the Blues are so delightful,
And someone's just scored a goal,
It's Andy Cole, Andy Cole, Andy Cole!

Come In A Taxi

(To the tune of 'Guantanamera')

Come in a taxi,
You must have come in a taxi,
Come in a taxi,
You must have come in a taxi!

*(Usually sung to teams with very poor away followings such as
Wimbledon in the 1980s and Fulham in more recent years)*

CTID

(To the tune of 'H-A-P-P-Y')

City till I die,
I'm City till I die,
I know I am, I'm sure I am, I'm City till I die.

*(Popular chant often over in seconds to re-affirm the
backing of the faithful during good times and bad)*

Curle, Keith

Ooh, Curly-Wurly,
Ooh, Curly-Wurly!

*(Basic but popular song for one-time
record signing Keith Curle)*

66 Our version of Blue Moon is sort of Public Image Limited-influenced. At first we thought it was way too psychedelic…it was a tricky one. We were happy to do it and all we need to do now is write a soundtrack for a David Lynch movie. He's not a City fan is he by any chance? 99

– Andy Williams, Doves

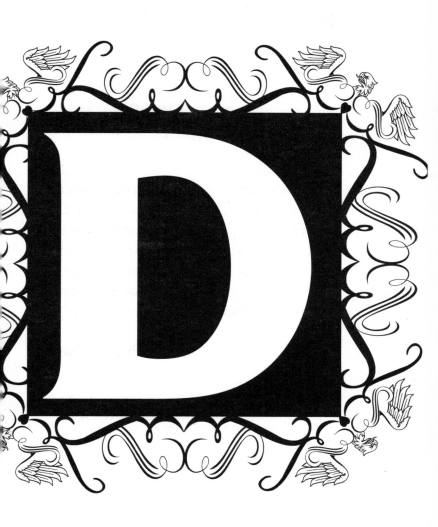

Davis, Wyn
(To the tune of 'The Mighty Quinn')

Come on without,

Come on within,

You'll not see nothing like the mighty Wyn!

Day Out
(To the tune of 'Tom Hark')

You've had your day out,

Now **** off home,

You've had your day out,

Now **** off home.

*(Blunt message to visiting teams as City's home record
improved markedly from 2010 onwards)*

De Jong Goes Sliding In
(To the tune of 'When The Saints Go Marching In')

Oh when De Jong (oh when De Jong),
Goes sliding in (goes sliding in),
Oh when De Jong goes sliding in,
There's only going to be one winner,
When De Jong goes sliding in!

(Popular chant for a popular player, the words have resonance in regards to the Holland midfielder's uncompromising tackling style)

De Jong, Nigel II

De Jong, De Jong, De Jong, De Jong, De Jong!
De Jong, De Jong, De Jong, De Jong, De Jong!
De Jong, De Jong, De Jong, De Jong, De Jong!

(War chant style backing of Dutch enforcer Nigel de Jong)

Derby Day
(To the tune of 'Mary's Boy Child')

My father said to me one day "is it red or blue for you?"
And if it's red you're out the door and I won't see you no more.
And then one Saturday afternoon he took me to Moss Side,
He said "my son your time has come and this is a lesson in pride.
You see the Reds you never run,
You stand and fight your ground,
And when you've won on derby day,
You're sure to hear this sound...
Hark now hear,
The City sing,
United ran away,
And we will fight for ever more,
Because of derby day!

*(The Boney M classic received the treatment to become a popular City song,
the last five lines often sung on their own in a shorter version)*

Dickov, Paul
(To the tune of 'Guantanamera')

One Paul Dickov,
There's only one Paul Dickov,
One Paul Dickov,
There's only one Paul Dickov,
One Paul Dickov, there's only one Paul Dickov! (etc)

Doyle, Mike
(To the tune of 'Who Do We Appreciate?')

M-I,
M-I-C,
M-I-C-K,
Mick Doyle!

(Popular chant for former skipper and hard man Mike Doyle)

Dunne, Richard

He's here, he's there, he's every ******* where,
Richard Dunne, Richard Dunne!

(A tribute to City skipper and four-times Player of the Year Richard Dunne and his ability to get around the pitch in City's cause, popping up at vital times with a willingness to put his body on the line)

Dunne, Richard II
(To the tune of 'Denis' by Blondie)

Dunney, Dunney, he'll put a crush on you,
Dunney, Dunney, he's over six-foot two,
Dunney, Dunney, he's coming after you-oooo.
And when he ran, was like a Chieftain tank,
And when he jumped, the ground beneath him sank.
Dunney, Dunney, he's coming after you-oooo.
Oh Dunney, Dunney's Blue, he's coming after you,
Dunney, Dunney's Blue, he's over six-foot two,
Dunney, Dunney's Blue, he'll put a crush on you-ooooooo.

*(Brilliant adaptation of Blondie's worldwide smash in
honour of City skipper Richard Dunne)*

Manchester City Songbook

Dzeko, Edin

Woah, oh-oh,
Edin Dzeko, oh-oh!
Edin Dzeko, oh-oh!
(Repeat until bored)

*(A difficult tune to describe! Edin Dzeko's chant can often be
heard echoing around the Etihad Stadium on a matchday)*

Dzeko, Edin II
(To the tune of 'Dynamite')

I throw my hands up in the air sometimes,
Singing Dzeko, Edin Dzeko!

*(Alternative Dzeko song to the tune of
Taio Cruz's worldwide hit)*

“ It's flattering to think the club and fans have chosen *'Pounding'* to help psyche the crowd up before games. I've been at the ground a few times when it's being played, but I stop short of tapping my foot to it – it's not the done thing! ”

– Andy Williams, Doves

66   I'd love the lads to run out to the first single off the new album *'Neat Little Rose'*; it's got a good beat behind it, and a good tempo to get the blood going 99

– Richard Jupp, Elbow

Elano

Jingle bells, jingle bells,
Elano's gonna score,
Oh what fun it is to see Robinho get two more...

(An affectionate tribute to the Brazilian midfielder who proved so popular with City fans during his two years with the Blues)

Elano II
(Tune of 'The Music Man')

Ela-Ela-Elano, Elano, Elano,
Ela-Ela-Elano, Elano, Elano!

Elano III
(To the tune of 'That's Amore!')

When the ball hits the net it's a pretty safe bet – it's Elano.
Left foot or right, the boy's dynamite – it's Elano.
The boy's from Brazil with a bag full of tricks – he's Elano...
When the ball hits the net it's a pretty safe bet – it's Elano!

*(First heard after Elano scored a stunning free-kick
against Newcastle United at the Etihad Stadium)*

Every Little Thing
(To tune of 'Three Little Birds')

City don't worry,
About a thing,
'Cause every little thing,
Is gonna be alright.
City don't worry,
About a thing,
'Cause every little thing,
Is gonna be alright.

*(A creation of the supporters group Blue Alliance, the Bob Marley classic
Three Little Birds has become a popular song in the latter half of the
2010/11 campaign. Tuneful, happy and positive, it can last for a few
minutes and is sung whether City are winning, losing or drawing)*

66 I really can't remember when I first heard the song *'Feed The Goat'* but I loved it. I recall the lads coming in at half-time and saying 'did you hear that song, Goat? They're singing about you,' and it just caught on. Some people reckon it was during the 4-0 win over Fulham, others in the away win at Forest – I don't know who thought it up, but I definitely owe them one. The fans would sing it when I scored and if I didn't find the net, I'd put in a few strong challenges and they'd start up again – I wanted to keep that song going! 99

– **Shaun Goater**

Feed The Goat

Feed the Goat, feed the Goat,
Feed the Goat and he will score!
Feed the Goat and he will score!

(One of the most popular chants of the past 50 years, 'Feed The Goat' was the serenading fans' anthem for terrace idol Shaun Goater. With a tune taken from a Welsh hymn, Goater, considered a journeyman striker when he joined City from Bristol City in 1998, gradually won over the supporters to the point he was revered as a playing club legend. His numerous goals won him wider recognition as a goal poacher par excellence and the dignity and humbleness of such a great goalscorer further endeared him to the Blues' fans and spawned 'Who Let The Goat Out?' and 'All I need is the air that I breathe (and Shaun Goater)'. 'Feed The Goat' appeared around 1999 and became a song popular throughout football. Still sung today and saved for special occasions, Goater and Feed The Goat are interwoven into the club's fabric and popular culture)

Ferdinand, Rio
(To the tune of Duran Duran's Rio)

His name is Rio and he watches from the stand,
Not such a bad way to collect a hundred grand,
And when he plays, he's really not that hard to beat,
In fact he's better off just watching from his seat!

*(Sung during Rio Ferdinand's lengthy ban for
missing an FA drugs test)*

Fergie's Cracking Up
(To the tune of 'Three Lions')

He's cracking up,
He's cracking up,
He's cracking,
Fergie's cracking up!

*(After Sir Alex Ferguson lost his cool and clashed with
Roberto Mancini during the 2011/12 Manchester derby,
this chant echoed around the Etihad Stadium for a few moments)*

Fergie's Cracking Up II
(To the tune of 'Give It Up')

Trainers with a suit, with a suit,
Trainers with a suit!
Na, na, na, na, na, na, na, na, nah.
Fergie's cracking up, cracking up,
Fergie's cracking up!

*(A variation on the previous song and sung around the same
time with reference to the United manager's odd
footwear alongside a smart suit)*

Fields Of Manchester
(To the tune of 'Fields Of Athenry')

Low lie the fields of Manchester,
Where once I watched the small Kinky play,
Colin Bell and Francis Lee,
Not forgetting Summerbee,
Oh there's no red in Manchester!

*(Not often heard of late but one of the few songs that links
players past with one from the more recent past)*

Fight Till The End

(To the tune of 'Sloop John B')

We'll fight till the end,
We'll fight till the end,
We're Man City,
We'll fight till the end!

*(A song borne out of City's refusal to give up
on the title race despite falling eight points
behind United with just six games to go)*

Fowler, Robbie

(To the tune of 'Yellow Submarine')

We all live in a Robbie Fowler house,
Robbie Fowler house,
Robbie Fowler house.
We all live in a Robbie Fowler house,
Robbie Fowler house,
Robbie Fowler house.
No.1 is Robbie's house,
No.2 is Robbie's house,
No.3 is Robbie's house,
No.4 is Robbie's house,
No.5 is Robbie's house.
We all live in a Robbie Fowler house,
Robbie Fowler house,
Robbie Fowler house.

*(Sung after revelations that Robbie owned more
than 80 houses in the North West)*

Fowler, Robbie II

Thank you very much for Robbie's wages,
Thank you very much,
Thank you very, very, very much.
Thank you very much for Robbie's wages,
Thank you very much,
Thank you very, very, very much!

*(There were rumours cash-strapped City had struck a deal
with Leeds United that the Elland Road club finance part of
the transfer of Fowler to Maine Road by subsiding his
wages in order to make the deal happen)*

“ I'd waited so long for this moment and after it taking so long to play a full game against United who represented a yardstick in English football as far as I was concerned. As a little kid in Bermuda, this was the team I wanted to play against because they were the team to beat – it may be Chelsea today, but it was United back then. We held out comfortably to win 3-1 and I walked off to an incredible rendition of *'Feed The Goat'* followed by 'Who let the Goat out? Heaven! ”

– Shaun Goater

Gaudinho, Maurizio
(To the tune of 'O Sole Mio')

Just one Gaudinho,
From Germany,
He has a fetish,
For your car keys,
He robs Lamborghinis,
He is Gaudinhooooo of Man City!

*(A song that emerged after reports City's on-loan
Maurizio Gaudinho had allegedly been involved
in car theft back in Germany – unproven!)*

Given, Shay
(To the tune of 'Volare')

He comes from Donegal,
He never drops the ball,
He's called Shaymus,
He's the famous,
City Wonderwall...

Goater, Shaun
(To the tune of 'The Air That I Breathe')

Sometimes,
All I need is the air that I breathe,
And Shaun Goater.

Goater, Shaun II
(To the tune of 'Who Let The Dogs Out?')

Who let the Goat out?
Who, who, who-who?
Who let the Goat out?
Who, who, who-who?
Who let the Goat out?
Who, who, who-who?
Who let the Goat out?
Who, who, who-who?

(This song had rumbled on for a few weeks but was sung by every City fan as the players left the pitch following the last Maine Road Manchester derby. City had won 3-1, Goater had scored twice and the goals were his 99th and 100th for the Blues)

Goater, Shaun III

Remember, remember the ninth of November,
The last Maine Road derby will last forever,
The score was level, the Goat fed by Neville,
Silly boy should have known for sure,
Feed the Goat and he will score.

Goater, Shaun IV

(To the tune of 'Jesus Christ Superstar')

Shaun Goater, superstar,
How many goals has he scored so far?
One or two, or maybe three,
But he scored with his *** and we're at Wem-ber-lee.

*(This song pays tribute to cult hero Shaun Goater and his ability
to score goals with every part of his anatomy – including one that
brushed off his upper body in the play-off semi-final against
Wigan to set up the 1999 third tier final with Gillingham)*

Goater, Shaun V

(To the tune of 'Come On Feel The Noize')

So come on feed the Goat,
Come on feed the Goat,
He wants goals, goals, goals!
He wants goals, goals, goals!
So come on feed the Goat,
Come on the feed the Goat,
He scores goals, goals, goals!
He scores goals, goals, goals!

*(Yet another Goater classic and arguably he has more catchier
songs than any other City player – this was heard emanating
from the North Stand after he'd scored during
a 4-1 win over Fulham)*

God Bless City
(To the tune of 'Only Fools And Horses')

Some championships, no Champions League,
Some FA Cup, No LDV,
We don't care, lose or draw,
You'll always hear the City roar,
God Bless Man City,
Viiiiiva Man City,
God bless Man City,
C'est Magnifique, Man City!
A proper club, Man City,
No cockney t**ts, Man City!
Man City!

(Improvised chant and not heard often but great lyrics!)

Gonna Get Along Without You Now
(To the tune of 'Gonna Get Along Without You Now')

You told everybody that we were friends,
This is where the friendship ends,
Aha, wo-oh, gonna get along without you now!
Aha, wo-oh, gonna get along without you now!

*(Intelligent dig at the media and other football fans who used
to call City their second club and retain affection for the Blues'
rollercoaster existence – until we became rich and successful)*

Greatest Of Them All

Some speak of Man United and Bolton as well,
Of Oldham and Bury,
I've also heard tell.
But the team to remember,
The team to recall,
Is Manchester City, the greatest of them all...
But the team to remember,
The team to recall,
Is Manchester City, the greatest of them all...

Haaland, Alfie
(To the tune of 'London Bridge')

Alfie Haaland is a Blue,
Is a Blue, is a Blue,
Alfie Haaland is a Blue,
He hates Man U.

Hareide, Aage
(To the tune of 'We Are The Champions')

Oggy Hareide!
Oggy Hareide!

Hart, Joe

England, England's number one,
England's number one!

Hart, Joe II
(To the tune of 'Ossie's Dream')

Joe Hart do the Poznan,
Joe Hart do the Poznan,
Na na na nah,
Na nan a nah.
Joe Hart do the Poznan,
Joe Hart do the Poznan,
Na na na nah,
Na nan a nah.

(Sung – usually by the South Stand – until Hart responds in some form)

Hartford, Asa
(To the tune of 'Roly Poly')

Oh Asa Hartford, Asa Hartford,
Na, na, na, na, na hey,
Oh Asa Hartford, Asa Hartford,
Na, na, na, na, na hey!

Hate Man United

As I was walking down the Claremont Road,
Without a penny in my kitty,
When a man said to me,
'Are you going to see?
The famous Manchester City!'

So I took my place upon the Kippax Street,
To see the famous Man City,
And when Colin Bell scored,
The crowd all roared,
For the boys in the sky blue jersey.

Well to Hell with Everton and Liverpool, too,
We'll throw them all in the Mersey,
And we'll fight, fight, fight,
With all our might,
For the boys in the sky blue jersey.

And we hate United and we hate their shirts,
Them load of b*****s should be wearing skirts,
If they brought back flogging,
They'd be the first,
'Cos we hate the Man United!

*(Songs this long are rarely heard on matchdays but make the odd
appearance in pubs, away ground or journeys to matches)*

Hello, Hello!
(To the tune of 'Billy Boys')

Hello, hello we are the City boys,
Hello, hello we are the City boys,
And if you are a Man U fan, surrender or you'll die,
We all follow Man City.

(Sung more often at Maine Road on the Kippax, the song lends itself to the Blues' protestant connections to Man United's more catholic links)

Hey, Scousers!
(To the tune of 'Hey, baby!')

Heeeeeeeey, hey, Scousers – ooh ah!
I wanna knoo-oo-oow where's my video..
And my stereo, and my DVD!

(Exclusively saved for visits or trips to Everton or Liverpool)

Horlock, Kevin

(Sung to the tune of 'Bobby Shafter')

Su-per, super Kev,
Su-per, super Kev,
Su-per, super Kev,
Su-per Kevin Horlock!

Huckerby, Darren

He can tackle,
He can jump,
He can run like Forest Gump,
Huckerby, Huckerby!

Huckerby, Darren II
(To the tune of 'Son Of My Father')

Oh, Darren, Darren!
Darren, Darren, Darren, Darren Huck-erby!
Oh, Darren, Darren!
Darren, Darren, Darren, Darren Huck-erby!

Hulk II
(To the tune of 'Tom Hark')

Spiderman's right,
You're f*****g s***e,
Spiderman's right,
You're f*****g s***e!

(More superhero stick for the big man from Porto!)

Hulk

You're not incredible,
You're not incredible,
You're not incredible,
You're not incredible!

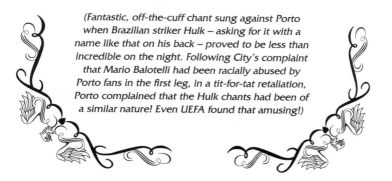

(Fantastic, off-the-cuff chant sung against Porto when Brazilian striker Hulk – asking for it with a name like that on his back – proved to be less than incredible on the night. Following City's complaint that Mario Balotelli had been racially abused by Porto fans in the first leg, in a tit-for-tat retaliation, Porto complained that the Hulk chants had been of a similar nature! Even UEFA found that amusing!)

66 The fans have been different class. I knew they would be because I know what they are like when you pull on that shirt. Once you pull on that City shirt and have that badge on your chest, you are one of them and as long as you perform and give everything that you have got, then they will accept you. You cannot ask for more than that. The lads have got to be humble by the way the supporters turn out every week for us and get behind us – I know that I am. Who knows what we can achieve together? 99

– Joey Barton

I Got Sunshine
(To the tune of 'My Girl')

I got sunshine on a cloudy day,
When it's cold outside,
I got the month of May.
I guess you say,
What can make me feel this way?
Cityyyyy!
Talking 'bout City, City!

If You Hate Man United
(To the tune of 'Aye, Aye Ippy')

If you hate Man United clap your hands *(clap clap)*,
If you hate Man United clap your hands *(clap clap)*,
If you hate Man United, hate Man United,
Hate Man United clap your hands.

*(Ever popular and, thankfully, ending as written above
– it wasn't always the case)*

In 1963...

In 1963 when we fell to Division Two,
The Stretford End cried out aloud,
'It's the end for you Sky Blue'.
Joe Mercer came,
We played the game,
We went to Rotherham,
And won 1-0,
And we were back into Division One.
We've won the league, we've won the League Cup,
We've been to Europe, too.
And when we win the l eague again,
We'll sing this song to you,
City, City, City, City, City!

*(Popular and long-lasting song that is still often heard – a real
passed down chant – from father to son or daughter!)*

Ireland, Stephen

Ireland is Superman,
Ireland is Superman,
Ireland is Superman,
Ireland is Superman!

(When Stephen Ireland suddenly found confidence in his own abilities, he became the most important player in the City side for 18 months before his form began to wane. With the chant well-established, after scoring one particular goal, Ireland dropped his shorts to reveal a pair of Superman trunks!)

Ireland's Granny
(To the tune of 'Molly Malone')

Alive, alive oh,
Alive, alive oh,
Stephen Ireland's two grannies,
Alive, alive oh!

(Brilliant chant which was first heard after it was revealed Ireland had left the Republic of Ireland squad after telling officials his grandmother had passed away. It was later revealed it was a ploy to return home and both his grans, thankfully, were alive and well and in rude health)

Istanbul

Istanbul, Istanbul we are coming,
Istanbul, Istanbul I pray,
Istanbul, Istanbul we are coming,
We are coming at the end of May.

*(Song that was sung during City's 2009/10 Europa League
run which was ended by Hamburg at the quarter-final stage
– another version along the same lines was chanted in
2010/11 with Dublin replacing Istanbul)*

Jingle Bells

Jingle bells,

Jingle bells,

Jingle all the way,

Oh what fun it is to see,

City win away!

[Repeat]

(Festive song usually only heard when the Blues have a two-goal cushion on the road – anything sooner would be tempting fate!)

Jingle Bells II

Jingle bells,

Stepney smells,

Crerand's on the booze,

Nobby Stiles has got no teeth,

And United always lose.

(Alternative early 1970s version of the previous song)

Joe Mercer's Aces
(To the tune of 'Blaydon Races')

Oh, me lads,
You should have seen them coming,
Fastest team in the land,
Should have seen them running,
All the lads and lasses, all with smiling faces,
Walking down to Maine Road,
To see Joe Mercer's aces!

*(Popular football chant adapted by each set of supporters who
sing it and undoubtedly originating from Newcastle United fans)*

Johnson, Adam
(To the tune of 'Can't Take My Eyes Off You')

Oh, Adam Johnson he plays in blue and white,
Oh, Adam Johnson, he'll play out left or right,
Oh Adam Johnson, makes your full-back look s***e.

*(Tribute to the box-of-tricks England winger Adam Johnson,
who has a penchant for tormenting defenders)*

Just Like Watching Brazil

(To the tune of 'Blue Moon')

Brazil,
It's just like watching Brazil,
It's just like watching Brazil,
It's just like watching Brazil.

*(No definitive date when first sang, but certainly first heard
to a national TV audience when a Georgi Kinkladze-inspired
City dismantled Oxford United 4-1 in 1996/97. Barnsley
later adopted the song as their own and won widespread
praise for it – but it began with City!)*

Karma, Karma, Karma C'mon City!
(To the tune of 'Karma Chameleon')

Karma karma karma karma karma come on City,
We're going up,
We're going up!

*(The Culture Club classic was at its loudest during City's
numerous promotion attempts during the 'yo-yo years')*

Keegan Wonderland
(To the tune of 'Walking In A Winter Wonderland')

There's only one, Kevin Keegan,
One Kevin Keegan,
We're walking along, singing this song,
Walking in a Keegan wonderland!

Keep The Blue Flag Flying High
(To the tune of 'Oh Christmas Tree')

Hello, hello, how do you do?
We are the boys in laser blue,
Wherever we go, we'll fear no foe,
'Cause the blue flags flying high,
Up flying high, up in the sky,
We'll keep the blue flag flying high,
From Manchester to the Bernabeu,
We'll keep the blue flag flying high!

Kidd, Brian

Kiddo, Kiddo, Kiddo!

Kippax

We are the Kippax!
We are the Kippax!

*(Still sung a decade after leaving Maine Road,
usually by the South Standers)*

Kippax II

If I die in the Kippax Street, ooh, ooh,
If I die in the Kippax Street, ooh, ooh,
If I die in the Kippax Street,
There'll be 10 Man U fans at my feet, ooh, ooh.
Use your head and use your fee, tooh, ooh,
Use your head and use your feet, ooh, ooh,
Use your head and use your feet,
And you won't die in the Kippax Street, ooh, ooh.

Kippax III

If you are sad and lonely and your heart skips a beat,
You might be in trouble if you walk down Kippax Street,
Walk into the Parkside and hear our famous roar,
Put two fingers up at the Reds,
— We are the Mercer boys.

Kompany, Vincent
(To the tune of 'Go West')

Vincent Kompany,
Vincent, Vincent Kompany,
Vincent, Vincent Kompany,
Vincent, Vincent Kompany,
Vincent, Vincent Kompany!

(Anthemic and uplifting song for the City skipper)

Kompany, Vincent II
(To the tune of 'The Addams Family')

He's big, he's tall, he's scary,
His head's not very hairy,
He makes defenders wary,
It's Vincent Kompany!

*(An affectionate chant, first heard at Sunderland during the
2009/10 campaign, for City's Belgian skipper)*

Lee, Francis
(To the tune of 'My Mammy')

Franny, Franny,
He'd walk a million miles,
To kick Nobby Stiles,
Oh, Franny!

Lee, Jason
(To the tune of 'He's Got The Whole World In His Hands')

He's got a pineapple,
On his head,
He's got a pineapple,
On his head,
He's got a pineapple,
On his head,
He's got a pineapple on his head!

(Nottingham Forest's Jason Lee never quite lived down the fact that he had a somewhat unusual hair design perched atop his head. It was a song that followed the hapless soul from ground to ground and one guy in the Platt Lane danced around with a raw chicken on his head when City played Forest in the late 1980s – nobody knows why!)

Leeds United

(To the tune of 'When The Saints Go Marching In')

Oh Elland Road (oh Elland Road),
Is full of sheep (is full of sheep),
Oh Elland Road is full of sheep,
It's full of sheep, sheep and more sheep,
Oh Elland Road is full of sheep!

Leeds United II

You're worse than Leeds United!
You're worse than Leeds United!

*(After an ultra-defensive Leeds United played City at Maine Road,
this chant was born. The Lilywhites had drawn 0-0 perhaps
half-a-dozen times during the 1981/82 campaign but left City with
a 1-0 defeat courtesy of a last-gasp Kevin Reeves winner. Any
team who bored the Kippax thereafter was treated to this song
and, in particular, for the next visit of Leeds United, the City fans
informed them that they were, in fact, worse than themselves!)*

Lescott, Joleon
(To the tune of 'Sloop John B')

He's top of the league,
He's top of the le-ee-eague,
Joleon Lescott, he's top of the league.

(Sang in response to any insulting songs aimed at Joleon)

Lescott, Joleon II
(To the tune of 'Ossie's Dream')

Lescott's going to Europe,
Lescott's going to Europe,
Na na na na,
Na na na na!

*(First heard away to Everton when the Goodison Park
faithful were firing pelters at the England defender)*

Macclesfield

Are you watching?
Are you watching?
Are you watching Macclesfield?
Are you watching Macclesfield?

(City fans won universal praise as the Blues slipped into the third tier of English football for the third time, despite leading 5-2 at Stoke City)

Maine Road

Maine Road, Maine Road what a wonderful place.
In organisation we set the pace.
We've forward and half-backs and full-backs, too,
All proud to be wearing maroon and sky blue!

Man City
(To the tune of 'Ant Music')

So come on down to Maine Road,

And do yourself a favour...

Your football's lost its taste,

So try another flavour...

Man City oi oi oi oi!

Man City oi oi oi oi!

*(Classic adaptation of a huge 1980s hit by
Adam and the Ants and popular for a short time)*

Man U
(To the tune of 'Camptown Races')

Man U is our name,

Man U is our name,

2-0 up and ****** it up,

Man U is our name.

*(A short-lived song aimed at Manchester United who
had led 2-0 against Barcelona only to lose the game 3-2)*

Manchester!
(To the tune of 'The Banana Splits')

Manchester, la, la, la!
Manchester, la, la, la!

Manchester Boy

We go down to Maine Road, we go for a ride,
We go to watch City, the pride of Moss Side.
We cheer on the Sky Blues, we cheer on our team,
We know that we can't lose, so we let off steam.

We go to away games, it's worth all the fare,
The guard pulls and wrecked trains, we just do not care.
We smash all the bulb lights, we break down the doors,
We go for a few fights, we break all the laws.

At Maine Road it's different, we treat it with care,
We never throw litter, we don't ******* swear.
Because it's my City, it's my pride and my joy,
And I'm just so glad I'm a Manchester boy.

Manchester City FC
(Sung to the tune of 'The Wild Rover')

And it's Manchester City,
Manchester City FC,
We're by far the greatest team,
The world has ever seen!

(An old, timeless favourite that has been sung for several decades)

Mancini, Roberto
(To the tune of 'Volare')

Mancini, who-oh-oh-ah,
Mancini, who-oh-oh-ah,
He came from Italy, to manage Man City.
Mancini, who-oh-oh-ah,
Mancini, who-oh-oh-ah,
He came from Italy, to manage Man City.

(Sung shortly after Mancini first arrived but delivered with much more gusto as he guided City to greater things as the months went by)

Mancini, Roberto II
(To the tune of 'Volare')

Mancini, who-oh-oh-ah,
Mancini, who-oh-oh-ah,
He came from Italy,
Has pasta for his tea,
Mancini, who-oh-oh-ah,
Mancini, who-oh-oh-ah!

(Slight variation on the previous song – a more fun version)

Marching In
(To the tune of 'When The Saints Go Marching In')

Oh when the Blues, go marching in,
Oh when the Blues go marching in,
I want to be in that number,
Oh when the Blues go marching in...

Marsh, Rodney
(To the tune of 'Son Of My Father')

Oh, Rodney, Rodney,
Rodney, Rodney, Rodney, Rodney,
Rodney Marsh.

*(Iconic chant sung during Marsh's mid-seventies heyday.
Simple, classy and befitting of his mercurial talent)*

MCFC

MC,
MCF,
MCFC,
OK!

MCFC II
(To the tune of 'Son Of My Father')

Oh Man City,
The only football team to come from Manchester!

MCFC - OK

Oh, we never win at home,
And we never win away,
We lost last week and we lost today,
We don't give a ****,
'Cos we're all p****d up,
MCFC – OK!

*(Truly a song of Manchester City and the supporters,
meaning – quite literally – that the fans don't care
what happens because they will always be there,
whatever the result)*

Mercer, Joe
(To the tune of 'Grocer Jack')

Joe Mercer, Joe Mercer,
Is it true what people say?
We're gonna win ...the Football League?

Merrily We Roll Along
(Tune of 'London Bridge Is Falling Down')

Merrily we roll along,
Roll along, roll along,
Merrily we roll along,
Up the Football League.

*(As the lyrics indicate, a gentle song from yesteryear
that has been condemned to history)*

Morrison, Andy
(To the tune of 'Son Of My Father')

Oh, Andy, Andy,
Andy, Andy, Andy, Andy Morrison!

Mourinho, Jose

Your suit's from Matalan,
Your suit's from Matalan,
Your suit's from Matalan,
Your suit's from Matalan.

*(Even 'The Special One' had to smile at the stick about his long,
black winter coat from the City fans on this occasion as
the Blues beat Chelsea at the Etihad Stadium)*

Nasri, Samir
(To the tune of 'True Faith')

He is extraordinary,
No 19 Samir Nasri,
He is poetry in motion,
Worth about a 100 million,
That's the price that we would pay,
To keep the other clubs away,
He's a joy when he starts to attack,
He's gonna skin both of your full-backs,
I used to think that we'd never sign players like Kun,
Only Chinese guys like that Jihai Sun,
With Samir Nasri, Silva and our Kun,
The Blues adventure has only just begun,
I used to think that the day would never come,
But now we've got Nasri and Kun.

Nasri, Samir II
(To the tune of 'Give it Up')

Na, na, na, na, na, na, na, na, na, na
Samir Nas-er-i, Nas-er -i,
Samir Nasri!

Nasri, Samir III
(To the tune of 'Ruby')

Sammy, Sammy, Sammy, Sammy!
Na-as-eri!
Sammy, Sammy, Sammy, Sammy!
Na-as-eri!

*(Thought up by none other than Micah Richards and aired
on City's website during an episode of Inside City)*

Nevilles
(To the tune of 'Aye, Aye Ippy')

If the Nevilles can play for England so can I,
If the Nevilles can play for England so can I,
If the Nevilles can play for England,
Nevilles can play for England,
Nevilles can play for England so can I!

*(Often heard on derby day and aimed at the Neville
brothers, Gary and Phil – obviously when they
both were playing for United)*

No Reds In Manchester
(To the tune of 'When The Saints Go Marching In')

Oh there's no red, in Manchester,
It's only home to Man City,
Oh there's no red, in Manchester,
It's only home to Man City!

The North Stand

Bertie Mee said to Don Revie,
Have you heard of the North Bank Highbury?
Don said no, I don't think so,
But I've heard of the North Stand, Maine Road.

“ I love the song *'Oh When De Jong Goes Sliding In'*! It's always great to have the appreciation of fans because it shows that you're working hard and doing well. When we get to Wembley in a final, I might give the fans a verse of it myself! ”

– Nigel de Jong

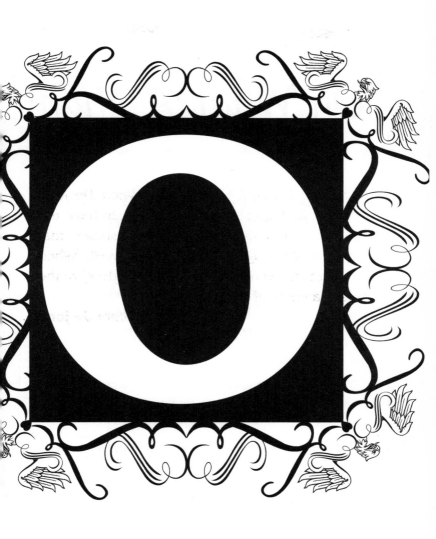

Oh What A Night

(To the tune of 'Oh What A Night')

Oh what a night,
One second half in two thousand and four,
Three-nil down and Joey shown the door,
I remember what a night!

Oh what a night,
Shaun Wright-Phillips showed you how it's done,
Distin, Bosvelt joined in on the fun,
I remember what a night!

Oh what a night,
Two minutes left before some extra-time,
Macken shows up on the six-yard line,
4-3 up oh what a night!

(First heard shortly after City's remarkable FA Cup 4th round replay away to Tottenham during which 10-man City went in 3-0 down at half-time only to win 4-3 on a dramatic night at White Hart Lane)

On Our Way

We're on our way,
We're on our way, we're on our way, we're on our way,
How we got here I don't know,
Will we stay there? I don't care,
All I know is City's on their way.

(First heard during the latter stages of the Blues' promotion push in 1999/2000 and sung with added gusto at the promotion party that was Ewood Park 2000 following City's 4-1 win over Blackburn)

Once A Blue...
(To the tune of 'Tom Hark')

Once a Blue,
Always a Blue,
Once a Blue,
Always a Blue,
Once a Blue,
Always a Blue.

(Sung on several occasions for different reasons – once it was for Wayne Rooney who had famously claimed the words of the song in connection with his Everton roots – before he signed for United. Other times it's been aimed at returning City players in the colours of other teams)

One, Two, Three...
(To the tune of 'Once I Caught A Fish Alive')

One, two, three, four, five,
We are City we will strive.
Six, seven, eight, nine, ten,
We are going to win again.
Who scored, was it Jo?
Elano or Robinho?
Defence, midfield, we will fight,
With Shaun Wright-Phillips on the right.

Only 6-1
(To the tune of 'Sloop John B')

It's only 3-1, it's only 3-1,
30,000 empty seats and it's only 3-1.
It's only 4-1, it's only 4-1,
40,000 empty seats, it's only 4-1.
It's only 5-1, it's only 5-1
50,000 empty seats, it's 5-1.
It's only 6-1, it's only 6-1,
60,000 empty seats, it's only 6-1.

*(The City fans enjoyed taunting United fans who were
leaving with City winning 3-1 and still 15 minutes to go.
The song developed as each goal went in!)*

Onuoha, Nedum
(To the chant of 'We Are The Champions!')

Nedum Onuoha!
Nedum Onuoha!
Nedum Onuoha!
Nedum Onuoha!

*(A simple chant sung for City's former Academy
graduate over a period of several years)*

Pardoe, Glyn
(To the tune of Heigh-ho)

Pardoe, Pardoe,

We're off to Mexico,

With Bell and Lee and Summerbee,

Pardoe, Pardoe, Pardoe, Pardoe...

*(Sung in 1970 as City fans voiced their expectation that unsung
hero Glyn Pardoe would earn an England call-up
for the Mexico '70 World Cup)*

Pardoe, Glyn II
(To the tune of 'The Mighty Quinn)

Come on without,

Come on within,

You ain't seen nothing like the mighty Glyn!

Pearce, Stuart

Psycho!
Psycho!
Psycho!

*(Inherited from his Nottingham Forest days where
he genuinely was Psycho in residence!)*

Pearce, Stuart II
(To the tune of 'Give Peace A Chance')

All we are saying,
Is give Pearce a chance,
All we are saying,
Is give Pearce a chance.

*(Classic re-working of the John Lennon classic as Stuart Pearce
stepped into the breach as caretaker manager
following Kevin Keegan's resignation)*

Phelan, Terry
(To the tune of 'You've Lost That Loving Feeling')

We've got that Terry Phelan,
Oh that Terry Phelan,
We've got that Terry Phelan,
And he's fast, fast, fast, woah-woah-woah.

(One of the best adaptations of a popular song, it was sung in honour of the rapid Irish international Terry Phelan during his time at City)

Portsmouth
(To the tune of 'Amarillo')

Sha la la la la la la la *(clap, clap)*,
Sha la la la la la la la *(clap, clap)*,
Sha la la la la la la la,
Harry Redknapp sh*t on you!

(As Portsmouth's travelling fans happily sang Amarillo during a visit to City, the Blues' fans came up with their own version following Harry Redknapp's decision to leave Pompey for Spurs)

The Poznan

(To the tune of 'Let's All Do The Conga')

Let's all do the Poznan,
Let's all do the Poznan,
Na, na, na, na!
Na, na, na, na!
Let's all do the Poznan,
Let's all do the Poznan,
Na, na, na, na!
Na, na, na, na!

*(The song that generally precedes a Poznan dance – often
just to liven things up and usually rounded off with
a hearty version of 'City! City! City!')*

Pride Of Manchester

(To the tune of 'Bread Of Heaven')

We're the pride,
We're the pride,
We're the pride of Manchester,
We're the pride of Manchester!

Pride Of Singapore

You're the pride,
You're the pride,
You're the pride of Singapore,
You're the pride of Singapore!

(City fans' dig at United's global following)

Que Sera, Sera

Que sera, sera,
Whatever will be, will be,
We're going to Wem-ber-ley,
Que sera, sera.

Que sera, sera,
Whatever will be, will be,
We're going to win the league,
Que sera, sera!

*(An old football chant and sung by many clubs who are in
with a chance of a trip to Wembley. It used to be sung with
scarves waved around in circles at head height)*

Niall Quinn's Disco Pants

Niall Quinn's disco pants are the best,
They go up from his arse to his chest...
They are better than Adam and the Ants,
Niall Quinn's disco pants!

*(Though later adopted by Sunderland fans, this song
was originally created by City fans during a night
out on a pre-season tour in Penola, Italy in 1992.
There had been a bust-up with City team-mate Steve
McMahon and Quinn had removed his torn and
bloodied shirt and was dancing with Rick Holden
wearing just a pair of cut-off jeans. He was unaware
that there were a group of hardcore City fans
watching and they treated him to what Quinn later
described as "the first performance of the song that
will follow me till the end of my career!")*

Quinn, Niall II
(To the tune of 'Ole, Ole, Ole!')

Ole, ole, ole, ole,
Niall Quinn, Niall Quinn!

Quinn, Niall III
(To the tune of 'The Mighty Quinn')

Come on without,
Come on within,
You've not seen nothing like the Mighty Quinn.

Remember When?
(To the tune of 'Remember Then')

Re-mem-mem, re-member-member,
Re-mem-mem, remember-member
Re-mem-mem, remember, member – when – when,
City scored ten?

*(This song refers to City's mammoth 10-1 win
over Huddersfield Town in 1987)*

Richards, Micah
(To the tune of 'Hey, Mickey!')

Hey Micah, you're so fine,
You scored a goal in injury-time,
Hey Micah! Hey Micah!

*(A certain situation or goal can spark a song – as in this case with
Micah Richards' injury-time equaliser at Aston Villa in 2007 spawning
a version of Toni Basil's 1980s hit 'Hey, Mickey!' Wasn't around
for too long but still fondly remembered.)*

Robinho

We've got Robinho, we've got Robinho,
We've got Robinho, we've got Robinho.

*(This song was famously first aired to a live audience of
millions at midnight on transfer deadline day 2008 as Sky
Sports News announced, live from the Etihad Stadium, that
the Brazilian star had joined the Blues from Real Madrid
just seconds before the window shut)*

Robinho II
(To the tune of 'Amarillo')

Show us the way to score Robinho,
You can even skin Evra and Rio,
Passing balls to Shauny and Castillo,
Oh our Robinho loves City.

Na na na na na na na nah, City!
Na na na na na na na nah, City!
Na na na na na na na nah,
Our Robinho loves City!

Robinho III

(To the tune of 'That's Not My Name' by Ting-Tings)

They call him skilful,
They call him great,
Manchester City,
We sing his name,
Robinho,
Robinho,
Robinho,
Robinho.

Robinho IV

(To the tune of 'Heigh-ho')

Heigh-ho, heigh-ho,
We've got Robinho,
With Petrov, Jo and Elano,
Heigh-ho, heigh-ho, heigh-ho, heigh-ho.

Robinho V
(To the tune of 'Volare)

Robinho whoah-oh, Robinho whoah-oh,
He came on deadline day!
He'll probably score today!
Robinho whoah-oh, Robinho whoah-oh!

*(Robinho – in regards to chants and songs,
he's the player who just keeps giving!)*

Robinho VI
(To the tune of 'Wheels On The Bus')

Robinho on the bus goes round and round,
Round and round, round and round,
Robinho on the bus goes round and round,
All day long.

*(When a newspaper reported Robinho was getting around
Manchester by taking the occasional bus trip, the City fans
loved the rumour and came up with this mini classic. He
later denies he'd been on the 42X to Didsbury – or any
other Manchester bus for that matter)*

Robinho VII
(To the tune of 'Oh Christmas Tree')

Robinho, Robinho,
You make Ronaldo look f*****g slow.
Robinho, Robinho,
You're our Brazilian dynamo.
So when we win the Premier League,
And when we win the Champions League,
There's only one song that we'll sing,
Robinho's our Brazilian king.

*(First heard when City travelled to play
Schalke in the Europa League)*

Ronaldinho
(To the tune of 'London Bridge Is Falling Down')

Ronaldinho is a Blue,
Is a Blue, is a Blue,
Ronaldinho is a Blue,
He hates Man U!

*(Sung in honour of Brazilian superstar Ronaldinho during a friendly
with Barcelona to open the Etihad Stadium. Ronaldinho – who had
just turned down a move to United – left the pitch to a standing
ovation and looked a little bemused by it all)*

Rooney, Wayne

He's fat,
He's Scouse,
He's gonna rob your house,
Wayne Rooney,
Wayne Rooney!

Rosler, Uwe
(To the tune of 'Go West')

Uwe, Uwe Ros-e-ler,
Uwe, Uwe Ros-e-ler,
Uwe, Uwe Ros-e-ler,
Uwe, Uwe Ros-e-ler!

*(Very popular song during the mid-to-late 1990s
in honour of German cult hero Uwe Rosler)*

Rosler, Uwe II

(To the tune of 'London Bridge Is Falling Down')

Uwe's grandad is a Blue, is a Blue, is a Blue,
Uwe's grandad is a Blue, he bombed Old Trafford!

*(Remembering United's ground had been bombed during
World War II, the City fans put two and two together)*

Ruining Football...

We're ruining football and we don't care,
We're ruining football and we don't care,
We're ruining football and we don't care,
We're ruining football and we don't care.

*(With City heavily criticised in all quarters for 'buying success', the
Blues' followers thought up this ironic chant which was basically
aiming two fingers at the numerous hypocrites in football)*

66 I appreciated the support of the fans very much. It was fantastic, of course it was. I had to stand up a few times from the bench to thank them, but I can do that. 99

– **Sven-Goran Eriksson**

Samaras, Georgios

Feed the Greek, feed the Greek,
Feed the Greek and he will score,
Feed the Greek and he will score!

*(Georgios Samaras' time with City barely merited such an
iconic chant, but such was the talent famine and lack of
goals during Stuart Pearce's reign as City boss, he was
treated to his own version of 'Feed The Goat')*

Santa Cruz, Roque
(To the tune of 'Santa Claus Is Coming To Town')

Oh! You better watch out,
You better not cry,
You better not shout,
I'm telling you why,
Santa Cruz is coming to town!

Better watch out!
Better beware!
He's good on the floor,
He's good in the air,
Santa Cruz is coming to town!

He's kicking the ball,
His shots are quite nice,
You never know if he'll score just once or twice,
Santa Cruz is coming to town.

*(Sadly, this song is the most memorable part of
Roque Santa Cruz's time with City!)*

Score When We Want
(To the tune of 'Sloop John B')

We'll score when we want,
We'll score when we wa-aa-aa-nt
We're Man City, we'll score when we want!

*(A City version of United's 'We'll Do What We Want', the song
was first heard during the 2011/12 season when City's
forwards were breaking all club scoring records)*

Sha-la-la-la Summerbee
(To the tune of 'Sha La La La Lee')

Sha-la-la-la Summerbee,
Sha-la-la-la Summerbee!
Who the f*****g hell is he?
The greatest centre forward in history,
United 1 and City 3,
Sha-la-la-la Summerbee,
He came to City from Swindon Town,
Sha-la-la-la Summerbee,
Little did they know he was England bound,
Sha-la-la-la Summerbee.

*(Popular version of the Small Faces' song in the late sixties for
charismatic City and England forward Mike Summerbee)*

Shall We Build A Ground For You?
(To the tune of 'Bread Of Heaven')

Shall we build a,
Shall we build a,
Shall we build a ground for you?
Shall we build a ground for you?

*(Sung to Everton fans during a time when there was
speculation they may be looking for a new home – it
was also heard at Anfield where Liverpool were similarly
believed to be looking to move to a new ground)*

Shall We Show You What To Do?
(To the tune of 'Bread Of Heaven)

Shall we show you?
Shall we show you?
Shall we show you what to do?
Shall we show you what to do?

*(When away fans celebrate goals with a mocking Poznan,
the City fans usually respond by doing a far
more polished demonstration)*

Sheikh Mansour
(To the tune of 'Kum Ba Yah')

Sheik Mansour, my lord, Sheik Mansour,
Sheikh Mansour, my lord, Sheikh Mansour,
Sheikh Mansour my lord, Sheikh Mansour,
Oh lord, Sheikh Mansour.

*(An homage to City's Abu Dhabi owner and
always sung with fitting reverence)*

Shinawatra, Thaksin
(To the tune of '500 Miles')

Oh you can freeze 500 million,
And you can freeze 500 more,
'Cos Thaksin's got another billion underneath his bedroom floor,
Shin-a-watra! Shin-a-watra!
Shin-a-watra! Shin-a-watra!

*(With Thaksin Shinawatra facing all kinds of charges
back in Thailand, City's millionaire owner faced an
uncertain future at the club. The fans reckoned it didn't
matter how many of his assets were frozen as he'd
have plenty more stashed away!)*

Should Have Been Ten!
(To the tune of 'Sloop John B')

It should've been ten,
It should've been te-e-en!
You lucky ********, it should've been ten!

*(City fans remind United fans that had the Blues taken all
their chances at Old Trafford, the 6-1 defeat could
have actually been far heavier)*

Silva, David
(To the tune of 'Hi Ho Silver Lining')

And it's, hi ho Silva's lightning,
Every time he plays its frightening,
I see that Blue moon rising,
But I won't make a fuss,
Because it's time for us.

Silva, David II

(To the tune of 'You Are My Sunshine')

Oh David Silva,
He drinks sangria,
He came to City,
To bring us joy.
He's five-foot seven,
He's football heaven,
So please don't take our Silva away.

(Adapted from Liverpool's classic song for Luis Garcia)

Silva, David III

(To the tune of 'The Great Escape')

His name is Silva, oh David Silva,
He scored the fifth goal at Old Trafford,
His name is Silva, oh David Silva,
He is the maestro of the Etihad.

*(The words are made to fit in yet another
tribute to City's brilliant Spaniard)*

Singing The Blues

I never felt more like singing the Blues,
City win, United lose,
Oh City,
You've got me singing the Blues!

*(Written and released in 1956, this is another old
favourite that has been around for a long time.
Popular and still heard on matchdays, 'Singing
The Blues' still holds resonance with the City fans
of today and if the results mentioned – City win
and United lose – actually occur,
the heartier the rendition!)*

Silva, David IV
(To the tune of 'Every Little Thing')

Every little thing he does is magic,
Every little thing he does is class,
And every goal that City score it's certain,
It is from a David Silva pass.

*(New song heard towards the end of the 2011/12 season
in reverence to the man Shaun Wright-Phillips
famously called 'Merlin')*

Sing When You're Fishing
(To the tune of 'Guantanamera')

Sing when you're fishing,
You only sing when you're fishing,
Sing when you're fishing,
You only sing when you're fishing!

*(City fans, bored during a dour game at Blundell Park,
playfully taunt the Grimsby Town fans)*

Sons Of MCFC
(To the tune of 'Sons Of The Sea')

City's the team,
We are the best team in the land,
Playing the game, always in command,
We may lose a point or two, but we never do despair,
'Cos you can't beat the boys in the old light blue,
When they come from Manchester.

*(A popular terrace chant in the 1940s and 1950s – and a
world away from the harsher songs of today)*

Stand Up!
(To the tune of 'Go West')

Stand up, if you love City,
Stand up, if you love City,
Stand up, if you love City,
Stand up, if you love City!

Sun Jihai
(To the tune of 'Aye Aye Ippy')

Singing aye, aye, ippy, Sun Jihai,
Singing aye, aye, ippy, Sun Jihai.
Singing aye, aye, ippy, his dad's got a chippy,
Aye, aye, ippy, Sun Jihai.

*(Chinese international Jihai Sun became something of a
cult figure during his time at City. The end result was this
amusing song that further increased Sun's popularity)*

Super City
(To the tune of 'Sailing')

We are City,
We are City,
Super City, from Maine Road,
We are City, Super City,
We are City, from Maine Road.

*(Based on Rod Stewart's huge hit, several clubs adopted the
tune to fit their club and City were no different. Still popular
today because of the Maine Road connotations, and because
ultimately, it is a great song to sing in a stadium)*

Sven-Goran Eriksson

Sven-Goran Eriksson,
Sven-Goran Eriksson,
Sven-Goran Eriksson,
Sven-Goran Eriksson!

Sven-Goran Eriksson II
(To the tune of 'The Wall')

We don't need no Phil Scolari,
We don't need Mourinho,
Hey! Thaksin! Leave our Sven alone!

*(When rumours surfaced that chairman Thaksin Shinawatra
was thinking of replacing popular City boss Sven-Goran
Eriksson towards the end of the 2007/08 season, City fans
came up with this clever take on Pink Floyd's classic)*

66   Yeah, I'd have a little jam with him. He can't speak English though – I've met him! But I love that he doesn't care and just goes out and does his thing. If he ever wants to bust the guitar out and do a bit, I'm always available! 99

– Noel Gallagher on Carlos Tevez

Take Me Home
(To the tune of 'Country Road')

Take me home to Maine Road,
To the place I belong,
On the Kippax,
To see the City,
Take me home to Maine Road.

(Direct response to Manchester United's song of a similar vein)

Taylor, Robert
(To the tune of 'Bobby Shafter')

Big fat, big fat Bob,
Big fat, big fat Bob,
Big fat, big fat bob,
Big fat Bobby Taylor!

(When Robert Taylor arrived at City from Gillingham at a cost of £2m, there were high expectations of what he could achieve having been a prolific scorer for the Kent club – but his time at City was marred by injury and disappointment with, as the song suggests, question-marks raised about his fitness!)

Ten Men Went To Mow

One man went to mow,
Went to mow at Chelsea,
One man and his baseball bat,
Went to mow at Chelsea.

Two men went to mow,
Went to mow at Chelsea,
Two men, one man and his baseball bat,
Went to mow at Chelsea.

Three men went to mow,
Went to mow at Chelsea,
Three men, two men, one man
and his baseball bat,
Went to mow at Chelsea.
Four men went to mow,
Went to mow to Chelsea,
Four men, three men, two men, one man
and his baseball bat,
Went to mow at Chelsea.

[continued...]

[...continued]

Five men went to mow,
Went to mow at Chelsea,
Five men, four men, three men, two men,
one man and his baseball bat,
Went to mow at Chelsea.

Six men went to mow,
Went to mow at Chelsea,
Six men, five men, four men, three men,
two men, one man and his baseball bat,
Went to mow at Chelsea.

Seven men went to mow,
Went to mow at Chelsea,
Seven men, six men, five men, four men, three
men, two men, one man and his baseball bat,
Went to mow at Chelsea.

Eight men went to mow,
Went to mow at Chelsea,
Eight men, seven men, six men, five men, four
men, three men, two men, one man
and his baseball bat,
Went to mow at Chelsea.

Nine men went to mow,
Went to mow at Chelsea,
Nine men, eight men, seven men, six men,
five men, four men, three men, two men,
one man and his baseball bat,
Went to mow at Chelsea.

Ten men went to mow,
Went to mow at Chelsea,
Ten men, nine men, eight men, seven men,
six men, five men, four men, three men,
two men, one man and his baseball bat,
Went to mow at Chelsea.
City! City! City! City!

Tevez, Carlos
(To the tune of 'London Bridge Is Falling Down')

Carlos Tevez is a Blue, is a Blue, is a Blue,
Carlos Tevez is a Blue,
He hates Man U!

*(When Carlos Tevez signed for City, this was the first and
most immediate song the City fans came up with)*

Tevez, Carlos II
(Tune the tune of 'God Save Ireland')

Who's that man from Argentina?
Who's that man you didn't sign?
He didn't sign for you,
'Cause his heart was set on Blue,
Now Carlos is City's 32!

*(A dig at the fact United failed to take up the option to sign Tevez
– a cult hero with United fans until his defection across the city)*

Tevez, Carlos III
(To the tune of 'Sloop John B')

He wants to go home,
He wants to go ho-o-ome,
Carlos Tevez, he wants to go home!

*(Following his self-imposed three month exile in Argentina during
the 2011/12 season, opposition fans began to sing the above
song, mocking the Argentinian's commitment to City. When
he began scoring goals for the Blues again, the City fans began
singing it, too, but with more than a little irony)*

Tevez, Carlos IV
(To the tune of 'The Animals Went In Two By Two')

He didn't want to play for you, Tevez, Tevez,
He didn't want to play for you, Tevez, Tevez.
He didn't want to play for you,
That's why he's gone from Red to Blue,
Carlos Tevez, City till he dies!

Tevez, Carlos V
(To the tune of 'Don't Cry For Me Argentina')

Don't cry for them Carlos Tevez,
The truth is they can't afford you,
All through the summer, where were you going?
We'll keep our Tevez,
You keep your Owen.

That's Amore!
(To the tune of 'That's Amore')

When your team it goes down,
And you still fill your ground,
That's amore!

When you go down again,
And you still fill it then,
That's amore!

*(City fans have remained loyal during the club's darkest days
and this song was hatched as a response to any opposition
fans who suggest City's gates were poor before the
Blues' more recent successes)*

The City Is Ours
(To the tune of 'Sloop John B')

The city is ours,
The city is ours,
Sod off back to London, the city is ours.

The Only... part 1
(To the tune of 'Son Of My Father')

Oh, Man City,
The only English team to win the championship.

*(A claim by City fans dating back to the late 1960s that no
other team has won the league title with
11 Englishmen – unconfirmed!!)*

The Only... part 2
(To the tune of 'Son Of My Father')

Oh, Man City!
The only football team to come from Manchester.

(A dig at United's countrywide support)

The Only Team
(To the tune of 'The Animals Went in Two By Two')

The only team in Manchester, City! City!
The best supporters in the world, City! City!
With pride in battle on our chest,
We'll fight to prove that we're the best,
Super City pride of Manchester!
Na, na, na, na, na, na, na, na, na, na, Na-nah!
Na, na, na, na, na, na, na, na, na, na, Na-nah!
Na, na, na, na, na, na, na, na, na, na,
Super City pride of Manchester!

There's A Hole...
(To the tune of 'There's A Hole In My Bucket')

There's a hole in the ceiling,
And the cantilever's leaking,
No money coming in...
Chuck the whole lot in the bin.

(Gentle song about United from the 1950s
– how times have changed!)

35 years
(To the tune of 'Tom Hark')

35 years, and we're still here,

35 years, and we're still here,

35 years, and we're still here,

35 years, and we're still here!

(A response that began with Manchester United fans taunting City supporters about the club's lack of silverware for so many years – but it backfired. The City fans used the song and slightly changed the lyrics to make it a proud testament of the City fans' unswerving loyalty over the four decades since the club last won a trophy. As the song says, 35 years and we're still here – would fans of certain other clubs have waited so patiently for success in such vast numbers?)

This Is How It Feels
(To the tune of 'This Is How It Feels')

This is how it feels to be City,

This is how it feels to walk tall,

This is how it feels when your club owes nothing at all,

Nothing at all.

Tiatto, Danny

(To the tune of 'The Music Man')

There is an Aussie man he plays in our team,
And when we see him play you will hear us sing
(what do we sing?)

Tia-tia, Tiatto, Tiatto, Tiatto,
Tia-tia, Tiatto,
Tia-Tiatto!

*(Sung during the 2001/02 season for tough-tackling
defender Danny Tiatto)*

Trick Or Treating
(To the tune of 'Guantanamera')

Gone trick or treating,
You should have gone trick or treating,
Gone trick or treating,
You should have gone trick or treating!

*(A song saved for when City are winning on Hallowe'en
night – it needs a particular set of circumstances and has
only been heard once or twice as a result!)*

Tueart, Dennis

Dennis Tueart, king of all Geordies!

U-N-I-T-E-D
(To the tune of 'This Old Man')

U-n-i-t-e-d,

That spells lots of debt to me,

With a nick-nack-paddy-wack give the dog a bone,

Get Ocean Finance on the phone.

*(With Manchester United reportedly £500m in debt at the time,
City fans advised the Reds to contact debt management experts)*

United Fans – Go On Home
(To the tune of 'Country Road')

Go on home, United Road,

To the place that you belong,

Down the M6 back to Essex,

Go on home, United Road.

66 I confess one thing, I'm glad to hear City fans at the stadium chant my name to the tune of 'Volare'. 99

— **Roberto Mancini**

Van Persie, Robin

(To the tune of 'Sloop John B')

Van Persie is ours,
Van Persie is ours,
Next transfer window,
Van Persie is ours!

(City fans taunt Arsenal fans after Samir Nasri's signing causes dismay among Gunners fans during the 2011/12 season – Van Persie had refused to commit to a new deal at the time)

Varadi, Imre

Imre, Imre Varadi,
Imre Varadi,
Imre Var-ah-ah-di – hey!'

(Russian Cossack theme for the cult late 1980s striker)

Vieria, Patrick
(To the tune of 'Sloop John B')

He's won it five times,
He's won it five ti-i-imes,
Patrick Vieira, he's won it five times!

*(This was Patrick Vieira's first City song and was heard, fittingly,
as he walked around the pitch at Wembley having won the
FA Cup for, as the song suggests, a record fifth time)*

Vieira, Patrick II
(To the tune of 'Volare')

Vieira, whoah-woah!
Vieira, whoah-oh-oh,
He came from Italy,
To play for Man City!

Vonk, Michel

Ooh, Vonky, Vonky,
Ooh, Vonky, Vonky!

66 I really like the desire the fans have to win something, and I sense that. It gives me a lot of strength. I know it is hard for people to go week-in, week-out; it can be expensive and it is not the main priority in life, but they make it their main priority. As a player, you can't ask for more than that. 99

– **Carlos Tevez**

Wanchope, Paulo
(To the tune of 'Top Cat')

Wanchope, the unbelievable Wanchope,
The irresistible, close friends get to call him Paulo,
Give him the ball and he will score you a goal,
Wanchope, the unbelievable, leader of our line,
He is top, he is hip, he is championship,
He's the one tip top, Wanchope!

*(Terrific take on cartoon Top Cat theme for
Costa Rican striker Paulo Wanchope)*

We All Follow...
(To the tune of 'Land Of Hope And Glory')

We all follow the City,
Over land and sea, and Stretford!
We all follow the City on to victory!

We Are The Kippax
(To the tune of 'The Mighty Quinn')

On top of all England,
Now stand the Sky Blues,
Who we will follow,
Win or lose.
'Cos we are the Kippax,
And when we cheer,
It sounds like music,
In Joe Mercer's ear.
So come on and join us,
We're here to stay,
Come on with the Sky Blues,
As we all say!

We Love You City
(To the tune of 'You Are My Sunshine')

We love you City, we do,
We love you City, we do,
We love you City, we do,
Oh City we love you!

We Were Here

We were here when we were s**t!
We were here when we were s**t!

Weaver, Nicky

Oh what a save,
Oh it's Nicky Weaver,
Oh what a save,
He's down to his left,
We went up ...woooooh,
It's Nicky Weaver what a 'keeper,
What a save.

*(Unusual song for City's former No.1 with
a complete dance to accompany it)*

Webb, Howard

He's big, he's Red, he sleeps in Fergie's bed,
Howard Webb, Howard Webb!

We'll Score Again...
(To the tune of 'We'll Meet Again')

We'll score again,
Don't know where, don't know when,
But I know we'll score again,
Some sunny day.

*(Sung during the darkest days of Stuart Pearce's reign when
City went an astonishing nine games without scoring a
Premier League goal at home)*

We'll Support You Evermore
(To the tune of 'Bread Of Heaven')

Man City, Man City,
We'll support,
We'll support,
We'll support you ever more!
We'll support you ever more!

We're Gonna Win The League
(To the tune of 'For He's A Jolly Good Fellow')

We're gonna win the league,
We're gonna win the league,
So now you gonna believe us?
So now you gonna believe us?
So now you gonna believe us?
We're gonna win the league!

*(Not heard for many years but sung at St James' Park after
City beat Newcastle 2-0 on the penultimate
game of the 2011/12 season)*

White, David
(To the tune of 'When The Saints Go Marching In')

Oh, David White (oh David White),
Is ******* fast (is ****** fast)
Oh David White is ******* fast, he's ******* fast,
fast and more fast,
Oh David White is ******* fast!

We're Not Really Here

(To the tune of 'We Shall Not Be Moved')

We are not, we're not really here,
We are not, we're not really here,
Like the friends of the Invisible Man,
We're not really here.

(There are more theories to this song than most, and anyone of them could be true. This song appears to have been inspired by City fans on tour in Ireland in the early 1990s who trashed the bar of the Metropole Hotel in Cork, then sung this impromptu song to the police officers sent to deal with the situation in the belief there was no proof as to which ones were responsible. It can't be ruled out! Whether that's true or not, we may never know, but the song really became popular on the terraces when the Blues slipped into the old Third Division for the first time in their history in the 1990s as an expression of bemusement at how a club of City's stature had managed to sink to an all-time low. Today, it is still sung with as much gusto at a packed City of Manchester Stadium as it was on the open terraces of places like Macclesfield Town and Lincoln City)

Whitley, Jeff

(To the tune of 'John Kettley Is A Weatherman')

Jeff Whitley is a clever man,
A clever man, a clever man,
Jeff Whitley is a clever man
And so is Stuart Pearce.

Who Put the Ball in United's Net?

(To the tune of 'Camptown Races')

Who put the ball in United's net?
Yaya, Yaya,
Who put the ball in United's net?
Yaya, Yaya Toure?
Who put the ball in United's net?
Yaya, Yaya,
Who put the ball in United's net?
Half the ******* team did!

Wiekens, Gerard

(To the tune of 'Winter Wonderland')

There's only one, Gerard Wiekens,
One Gerard Wiekens,
We're walking along,
Singing this song,
Walking in a Wiekens wonderland!

Will You Walk Down
To Maine Road With Me?

Will you walk down to Maine Road with me, son?
Will you walk down to Maine Road with me?
Will you walk down to Maine Road with me, son?
For a Sky Blue you're destined to be.

And as you first set sight on the floodlights,
Under a greying Mancunian sky,
Then you'll feel the same way as your dad did,
And for City you gladly will die.

And the scum from Old Trafford may call you,
Your friends and acquaintances, too,
But stand side by side by your old man,
And scream that you're proud to be a Blue.

And to all the Red *******s from Salford,
The team that we cannot abide,
We'll stand strong 'cos we come from Manchester,
And follow the team from Moss Side.

And if you become a father like I did,
Tell your children of their grandfather's side,
So that if I kick the bucket tomorrow,
They'll think of my memory with pride...
CITY CITY CITY CITY CITY!

WonderBall

(To the tune of 'Wonderwall')

And all the runs that Kinky makes are winding,
And all the goals that City score are blinding,
There are many times that we would like to score again,
But we don't know how,
'Cos maybe,
Eike's gonna be the one to save me (save me),
And after all,
You're my Alan Ball!

*(Perhaps one of the most famous, if short-lived, of City songs.
Adapted from the Oasis classic of the day, it actually serenaded
manager Alan Ball who was in the process of taking the Blues
down from the Premier League and wasn't actually that popular.
However, the lyrics and tune were too good not to sing and the
song was written about at length in the papers – even if it didn't
sit that comfortably with the majority of City fans)*

Worst Support
(To the tune of 'Bread Of Heaven')

Worst support,

Worst support,

Worst support we've ever seen,

Worst support we've ever seen!

*(Usually saved for the travelling Manchester United fans,
but not exclusively used against the Reds – sang to any side
with a quiet or sparse away following – as well as some
home supporters on City's travels!)*

Wright-Phillips, Shaun
(To the tune of 'Hot, Hot, Hot!')

Shauny Wright-Wright-Wright,

Shauny Wright-Wright-Wright!

Wright-Phillips, Shaun II
(To the tune of 'Bobby Shafter')

Shaun Wright-Phillips is ****** brilliant,
We sold him on for £20 million,
Brought him back for just a million,
Stupid Chelsea *******s.

*(When Shaun Wright-Phillips re-joined City for half the price
he left for, this song emerged for a brief time, suggesting
Chelsea's business sense was not all it should be)*

Wright-Phillips, Shaun III
(To the tune of 'Three Lions')

He's coming home,
He's coming home.
He's coming, Shauny's coming home!
He's coming home,
He's coming home,
He's coming, Shauny's coming home!

*(Sung when the news Shaun Wright-Phillips was
about to re-sign for City in 2009)*

Yaya And Kolo

(To the tune of 'No Limits')

Yaya, Yaya-Yaya, Yaya-Yaya, Yaya, Yaya Toure.
Kolo, Kolo-Kolo, Kolo-Kolo, Kolo, Kolo Toure.

Yaya Toure

(To the tune of 'Hey Jude' by The Beatles)

Ya, Ya, Ya,
Yaya-Ya Ya,
Yaya-Ya-Ya,
Tou-re!

*(Belted out often in honour of City's brilliant Ivorian
powerhouse Yaya Toure and sung loudly during the
Manchester derby of April 2012)*

Yaya Toure II

(To the tune of 'Camptown Races')

Who put the ball in United's net?
Yaya, Yaya,
Who put the ball in United's net?
Yaya, Yaya Toure!

Yaya Toure III

(To the tune of 'Camptown Races')

Who put the ball in the Scousers' net?
Yaya, Yaya,
Who put the ball in the Scousers' net?
Yaya, Yaya Toure!

Yaya Toure IV
(To the tune of 'Delilah')

Yaya, Yaya Toure,

Yaya, Yaya Toure,

So just before,

You break away and you score,

Oh Yaya Toure I think we should pay you some more!

*(Great adaptation of Stoke City's Tom Jones anthem
and yet another Yaya Toure tribute song)*

Yaya Toure V
(To the tune of 'Sunday, Bloody Sunday')

I can't believe the news today.

An eight point lead has gone, they've thrown it all away,

How long, how long have we waited now?

How long, how long?

Toure!

Yaya, Yaya Toure,

Yaya, Yaya Toure!

*(Some songs can only be sung for a limited time and
this one emerged after City ate United's eight-point
lead away during the 2011/12 title race run-in)*

Yaya Toure VI

(To the tune of 'Knowing Me, Knowing You')

Knowing me, knowing you – Yaya,
We're gonna make you a Blue,
Knowing me, knowing you – Yaya,
We are gonna sign him this time, it's true,
Knowing me, knowing you, we will make him a Blue.

You Are My City

(To the tune of 'You Are My Sunshine')

You are my City, my only City,
You make me happy,
When skies are grey,
You'll never know just,
How much I love you,
So please don't take my City away.
Nah, nah, nah, nah-nah-ooh!

*(A general uplifting song, usually heard when the team are playing
well or are winning. Written in 1939, it has been around a long
time and therefore difficult to pin a time down when it was first
sung. Still popular and has stood the test of time)*

You're In Debt

You're in debt,
You're in debt,
And it's growing,
You're in debt and you can't pay,

You're in debt,
You're in debt,
And it's growing,
You'll be bankrupt at the end of May...

(Another take on Manchester United's sizeable debt!)

Zabaleta, Pablo

(To the tune of 'Do The Conga')

Do, do, do,
Pablo Zabaleta,
Do, do, do,
Pablo Zabaleta!

(The Argentinian man of steel has several songs in his honour but this one is the most popular – to the Black Lace hit that also became The Trainline's TV advert jingle)

Zabaleta, Pablo II

(To the tune of 'Hey, Macarena!')

One Zaba,
Two Zaba,
Three Zabaleta.
Four Zaba,
Five Zaba,
Six Zabaleta.
Seven Zaba,
Eight Zaba,
Nine Zabaleta...
Hey, Zabaleta!

CHAMPION'S SONGSHEET 2011/2012

The hymns that echoed around Manchester as City brought their 44-year title wait to an end…

(To the tune of 'Volare')

Aguero, whoa-oh, Aguero, whoah-oh,
He is an Argentine,
He scored in Fergie time!

*(First heard at the Manchester Senior Cup final
a few days after the Blues' title triumph)*

(To the tune of 'Tom Hark')

We won the league,
In Fergie time,
We won the league,
In Fergie time

(First head as City toured Manchester city centre on an open top bus)

Championi, Championi,
Ole, ole, ole!
Championi, Championi,
Ole, ole, ole!

(Sung as City lifted the Premier League trophy for the first time)

" I'm still flabbergasted at the reception I receive each time and I still think, even today, that I have been a very lucky man. I've been lucky enough to play in front of the most magnificent fans in the world. "

– Bert Trautmann

Song Index

- Castillo, Nery
- Chelsea
- Christmas Shopping
- City Is Our Name
- City Is The Team
- City Will Win The League (1968)
- Clichy, Gael
- Clichy, Gael II
- Cole, Andy
- Cole, Andy II
- Cole, Andy III
- Come In A Taxi
- CTID
- Curle, Keith

- Davis, Wyn
- Day Out
- De Jong Goes Sliding In
- De Jong, Nigel II
- Derby Day
- Dickov, Paul
- Doyle, Mike
- Dunne, Richard
- Dunne, Richard II
- Dzeko, Edin
- Dzeko, Edin II

Index

- Elano
- Elano II
- Elano III
- Every Little Thing

- Feed The Goat
- Ferdinand, Rio
- Fergie's Cracking Up
- Fergie's Cracking Up II
- Fields Of Manchester
- Fight Till The End
- Fowler, Robbie
- Fowler, Robbie II

- Gaudinho, Maurizio
- Given, Shay
- Goater, Shaun
- Goater, Shaun II
- Goater, Shaun III
- Goater, Shaun IV
- Goater, Shaun V
- God Bless City
- Gonna Get Along Without You Now
- Greatest of Them All

Index

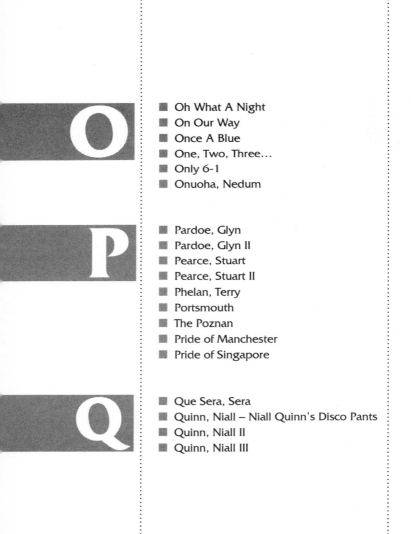

Index

66 I like the song the City fans sing for me – it's original, too! In Argentina, it was 'Agüero, Agüero', while in Spain they chanted 'Kun, Kun, Kun...' And now it's the 'Sergio, Sergio' – that was all that had been missing. I like how the City fans say it – it's pronounced 'SEHR-hee-oh' in Spanish, and it's fun to hear the Mancunians' 'SEHR-gee-o.' I know the fans can come up with new songs on their own and I'll always welcome any new ones. 99

– **Sergio Aguero**

❝ The fans are absolutely unbelievable at this club and I owe them so much. **❞**

– Georgi Kinkladze

❝ I want to win a lot of trophies with this club. I think our fans are incredible and it makes me more determined than ever to bring them success – when we win our first trophy it will be a very good moment for everyone, I think. **❞**

– Roberto Mancini

MANCHESTER
CITY
SONGBOOK

FROM BLUE MOON TO NIALL QUINN'S DISCO PANTS